By
Anthony Tallarico

Copyright © 1992 Kidsbooks, Inc. and Anthony Tallarico
7004 N. California Avenue
Chicago, IL 60645

ISBN: 0-8317-4982-2

This edition published in 1992 by SMITHMARK Publishers, Inc.,
16 East 32nd Street, New York, N.Y. 10016

SMITHMARK books are available for bulk purchase for sales promotion and premium use.
For details write or telephone the Manager of Special Sales, SMITHMARK Publishers, Inc.,
16 East 32nd Street, New York, N.Y. 10016 (212) 532-6600

Manufactured in the United States of America

WALT DISNEY WORLD

Walt Disney World is the fulfillment of Walt Disney's dream. He wanted to create the ultimate amusement park where adults and children could have fun together. Today, Walt Disney World in Florida is the most popular man-made attraction in the world and is visited by thousands of people every day.

See if you can find all the things you did or didn't know about Walt Disney World in this picture. Don't forget to look for the following fun things, too!

- ☐ Arrow
- ☑ Balloon
- ☐ Cake
- ☐ Chef's hat
- ☐ Clown
- ☐ Crown
- ☐ Drummer
- ☑ Elephants (2)
- ☑ Fish
- ☐ Football
- ☐ Football player
- ☐ Ghost
- ☐ Hammock
- ☐ Hearts (3)
- ☐ Horse
- ☐ Horseshoe
- ☐ Ice-cream cone
- ☑ Jack-o´-lantern
- ☐ Kite
- ☐ Ladder
- ☐ Lion
- ☐ Magnifying glass
- ☐ Pencil
- ☐ Penguin
- ☐ Snowman
- ☐ Telescope
- ☐ TV set

Who starred in "Steamboat Willie"?
On what day is Walt Disney World busiest?

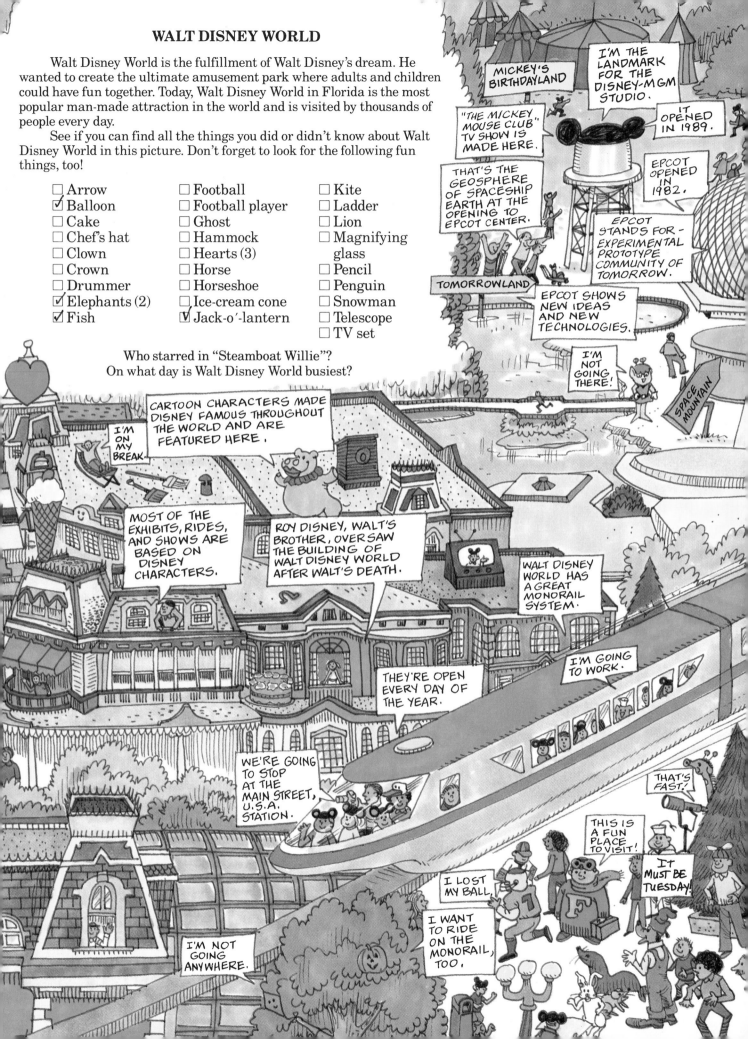

SACAGAWEA

Sacagawea (SAK-uh-juh-WEE-uh) was born among the Shoshone (show-SHOW-nee) Indians. As a young girl she was captured by an enemy tribe and sold as a slave to a trader who joined the Lewis and Clark expedition. Sacagawea became the principle guide for the expedition as they made their way across western lands to the Pacific Ocean and back again in 1804 and 1805. Historians have called Sacagawea one of the six most important American women of all time.

See if you can find all the things you did or didn't know about Sacagawea in this picture. Don't forget to look for the following fun things, too!

☐ Armadillo
☐ Arrows (2)
☐ Baby
☐ Bears (2)
☐ Beaver
☐ Bow

☐ Buffalo
☐ Coyote
☐ Deer
☐ Drum
☐ Eagle
☐ Egg

☐ Flying bat
☐ Flying saucer
☐ Frog
☐ Groundhog
☐ Heart
☐ Lost boot

☐ Moose
☐ Mountain goat
☐ Mushroom
☐ Owl
☐ Rabbits (3)
☐ Sailboat

☐ Skunk
☐ Snake
☐ Spear
☐ Turtle
☐ Wild turkey

What does Sacagawea mean?
Why did she agree to guide Lewis and Clark

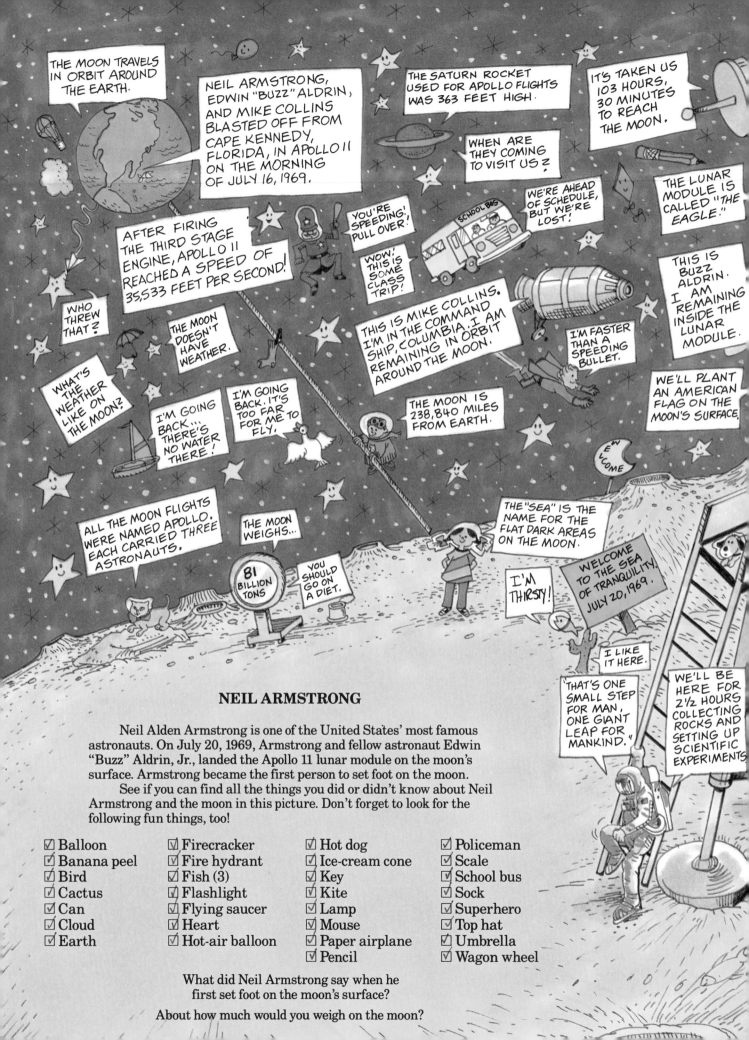

NEIL ARMSTRONG

Neil Alden Armstrong is one of the United States' most famous astronauts. On July 20, 1969, Armstrong and fellow astronaut Edwin "Buzz" Aldrin, Jr., landed the Apollo 11 lunar module on the moon's surface. Armstrong became the first person to set foot on the moon.

See if you can find all the things you did or didn't know about Neil Armstrong and the moon in this picture. Don't forget to look for the following fun things, too!

- ☑ Balloon
- ☑ Banana peel
- ☑ Bird
- ☑ Cactus
- ☑ Can
- ☑ Cloud
- ☑ Earth
- ☑ Firecracker
- ☑ Fire hydrant
- ☑ Fish (3)
- ☑ Flashlight
- ☑ Flying saucer
- ☑ Heart
- ☑ Hot-air balloon
- ☑ Hot dog
- ☑ Ice-cream cone
- ☑ Key
- ☑ Kite
- ☑ Lamp
- ☑ Mouse
- ☑ Paper airplane
- ☑ Pencil
- ☑ Policeman
- ☑ Scale
- ☑ School bus
- ☑ Sock
- ☑ Superhero
- ☑ Top hat
- ☑ Umbrella
- ☑ Wagon wheel

What did Neil Armstrong say when he
first set foot on the moon's surface?

About how much would you weigh on the moon?

WASHINGTON, D.C.

George Washington envisioned a city of beauty and stature for the new nation's capital when he chose Pierre L'Enfant, a French architect/engineer, to design it in 1790. Today's Washington, D.C. is certainly that. It has wide, straight avenues, lush parks, towering monuments, and beautiful trees and flowers.

Washington is also the political center of the nation. Here decisions are made in both the White House, the home of the President, and in the Capitol, the home of the Senate and House of Representatives, which affect the lives of millions of people.

This picture shows postcards from a class trip. See if you can find all the things you did or didn't know about Washington, D.C. Don't forget to look for the following fun things, too!

- ☐ Balloon
- ☐ Baseball cap
- ☐ Bird
- ☐ Brush
- ☐ Cactus
- ☐ Fish
- ☐ Fishbowl
- ☐ Flags (3)
- ☐ Flower
- ☐ Headband
- ☐ Key
- ☐ Kite
- ☐ Mouse
- ☐ Painted egg
- ☐ Scarves (2)
- ☐ Star
- ☐ Three-cornered hats (2)
- ☐ Top Hat

When did the U.S. government move to Washington, D.C.?

What is the purpose of the city of Washington?

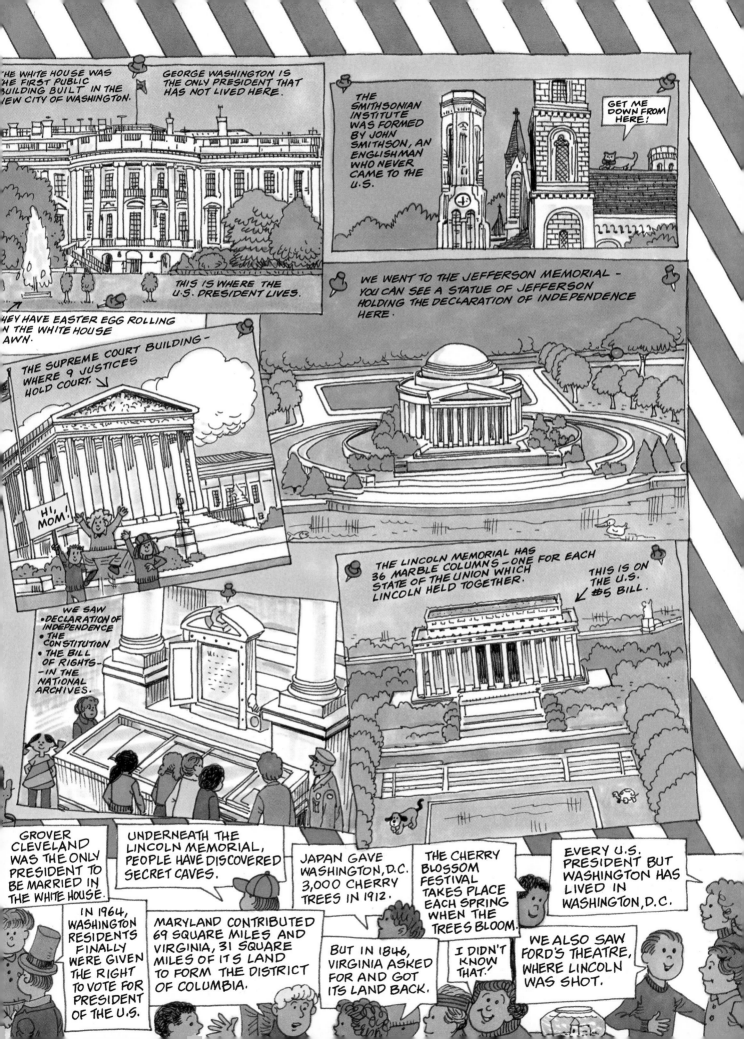

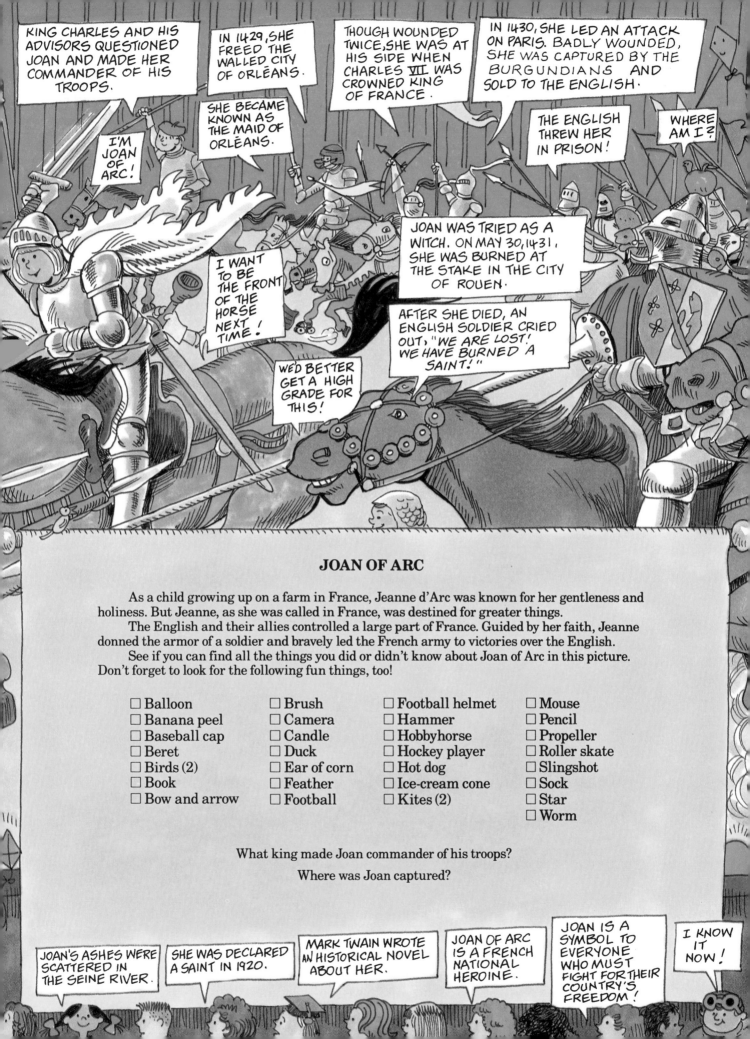

JOAN OF ARC

As a child growing up on a farm in France, Jeanne d'Arc was known for her gentleness and holiness. But Jeanne, as she was called in France, was destined for greater things.

The English and their allies controlled a large part of France. Guided by her faith, Jeanne donned the armor of a soldier and bravely led the French army to victories over the English.

See if you can find all the things you did or didn't know about Joan of Arc in this picture. Don't forget to look for the following fun things, too!

- ☐ Balloon
- ☐ Banana peel
- ☐ Baseball cap
- ☐ Beret
- ☐ Birds (2)
- ☐ Book
- ☐ Bow and arrow
- ☐ Brush
- ☐ Camera
- ☐ Candle
- ☐ Duck
- ☐ Ear of corn
- ☐ Feather
- ☐ Football
- ☐ Football helmet
- ☐ Hammer
- ☐ Hobbyhorse
- ☐ Hockey player
- ☐ Hot dog
- ☐ Ice-cream cone
- ☐ Kites (2)
- ☐ Mouse
- ☐ Pencil
- ☐ Propeller
- ☐ Roller skate
- ☐ Slingshot
- ☐ Sock
- ☐ Star
- ☐ Worm

What king made Joan commander of his troops?

Where was Joan captured?

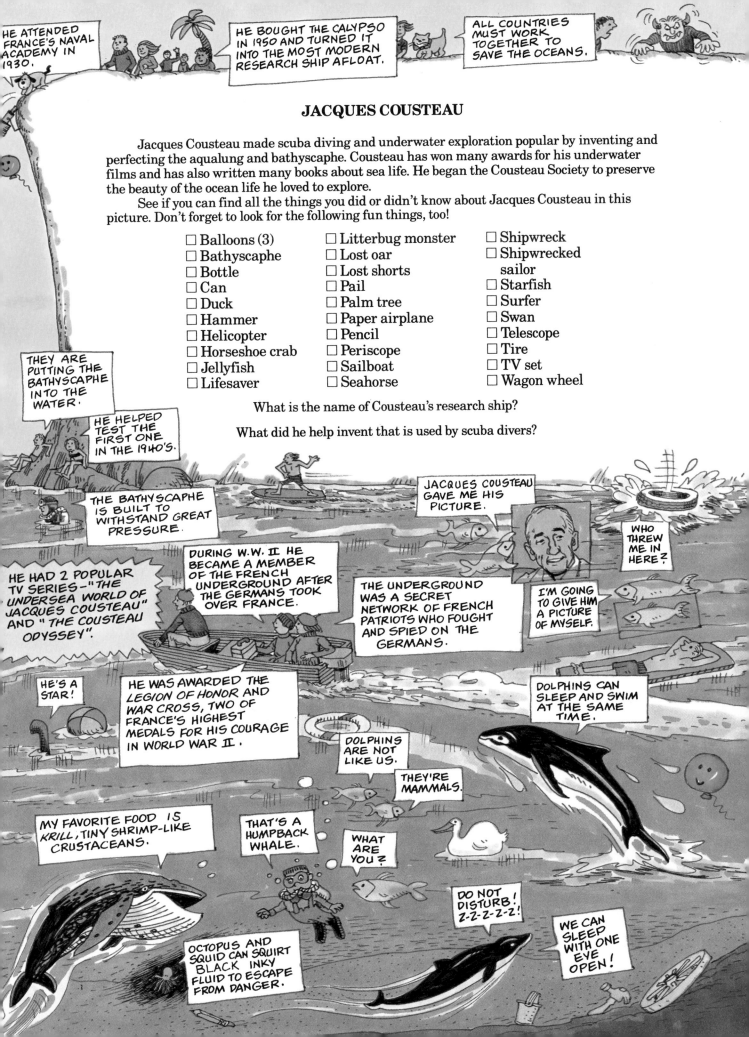

JACQUES COUSTEAU

HE ATTENDED FRANCE'S NAVAL ACADEMY IN 1930.

HE BOUGHT THE CALYPSO IN 1950 AND TURNED IT INTO THE MOST MODERN RESEARCH SHIP AFLOAT.

ALL COUNTRIES MUST WORK TOGETHER TO SAVE THE OCEANS.

Jacques Cousteau made scuba diving and underwater exploration popular by inventing and perfecting the aqualung and bathyscaphe. Cousteau has won many awards for his underwater films and has also written many books about sea life. He began the Cousteau Society to preserve the beauty of the ocean life he loved to explore.

See if you can find all the things you did or didn't know about Jacques Cousteau in this picture. Don't forget to look for the following fun things, too!

☐ Balloons (3)
☐ Bathyscaphe
☐ Bottle
☐ Can
☐ Duck
☐ Hammer
☐ Helicopter
☐ Horseshoe crab
☐ Jellyfish
☐ Lifesaver

☐ Litterbug monster
☐ Lost oar
☐ Lost shorts
☐ Pail
☐ Palm tree
☐ Paper airplane
☐ Pencil
☐ Periscope
☐ Sailboat
☐ Seahorse

☐ Shipwreck
☐ Shipwrecked sailor
☐ Starfish
☐ Surfer
☐ Swan
☐ Telescope
☐ Tire
☐ TV set
☐ Wagon wheel

What is the name of Cousteau's research ship?

What did he help invent that is used by scuba divers?

THEY ARE PUTTING THE BATHYSCAPHE INTO THE WATER.

HE HELPED TEST THE FIRST ONE IN THE 1940'S.

THE BATHYSCAPHE IS BUILT TO WITHSTAND GREAT PRESSURE.

JACQUES COUSTEAU GAVE ME HIS PICTURE.

WHO THREW ME IN HERE?

HE HAD 2 POPULAR TV SERIES—"THE UNDERSEA WORLD OF JACQUES COUSTEAU" AND "THE COUSTEAU ODYSSEY".

DURING W.W. II HE BECAME A MEMBER OF THE FRENCH UNDERGROUND AFTER THE GERMANS TOOK OVER FRANCE.

THE UNDERGROUND WAS A SECRET NETWORK OF FRENCH PATRIOTS WHO FOUGHT AND SPIED ON THE GERMANS.

I'M GOING TO GIVE HIM A PICTURE OF MYSELF.

HE'S A STAR!

HE WAS AWARDED THE LEGION OF HONOR AND WAR CROSS, TWO OF FRANCE'S HIGHEST MEDALS FOR HIS COURAGE IN WORLD WAR II.

DOLPHINS ARE NOT LIKE US.

THEY'RE MAMMALS.

DOLPHINS CAN SLEEP AND SWIM AT THE SAME TIME.

MY FAVORITE FOOD IS KRILL, TINY SHRIMP-LIKE CRUSTACEANS.

THAT'S A HUMPBACK WHALE.

WHAT ARE YOU?

DO NOT DISTURB! Z-Z-Z-Z-Z!

WE CAN SLEEP WITH ONE EYE OPEN!

OCTOPUS AND SQUID CAN SQUIRT BLACK INKY FLUID TO ESCAPE FROM DANGER.

NEW YORK CITY

New York City is the largest city in the United States and the fifth largest in the world. It is a universal center for art, fashion, architecture, finance, publishing, and more. A great deal of what happens in New York affects what happens around the country and even around the world!

See if you can find all the things you did or didn't know about New York City in this picture. Don't forget to look for the following fun things, too!

- ☐ Airplanes (2)
- ☐ Apple
- ☐ Baseball
- ☐ Bird
- ☐ Blimp
- ☐ Book
- ☐ Boom box
- ☐ Container ship
- ☐ Diver
- ☐ Ferry
- ☐ Fish
- ☐ Flower
- ☐ Flying saucer
- ☐ Football
- ☐ Ghost
- ☐ Heart
- ☐ Helicopter
- ☐ Hot-air balloon
- ☐ King Kongs (2)
- ☐ Kite
- ☐ Parachutist
- ☐ Periscope
- ☐ Rocking chair
- ☐ Rowboat
- ☐ Star
- ☐ Telescope
- ☐ Tire
- ☐ Top hat
- ☐ Tugboat
- ☐ Worm

Who first settled New York?
When was New York City the nation's capital?

I AM ON TOP OF THE WORLD TRADE CENTER'S TWIN TOWERS—110 STORIES TALL!

OVER 75 LANGUAGES ARE SPOKEN HERE.

BROADWAY RUNS FROM ONE END OF MANHATTAN TO THE OTHER.

MANHATTAN IS A NATIVE AMERICAN NAME MEANING "ISLAND OF THE HILLS."

IT'S THE SAME TRAIL THE FIRST NATIVE AMERICANS FOLLOWED, HUNDREDS OF YEARS AGO.

IT'S SO BIG IT HAS ITS OWN ZIP CODE.

ITS A NICE PLACE TO VISIT.

THE FIRST SUBWAY IN NEW YORK CITY WAS BUILT IN 1904.

OVER 17 MILLION PEOPLE VISIT EACH YEAR.

NEW YORK CITY IS MADE UP OF FIVE BOROUGHS.

THIS IS THE PLACE.

OVER 7 MILLION PEOPLE LIVE HERE.

A BOROUGH IS A SELF-GOVERNING ADMINISTRATIVE UNIT.

NEW YORK CITY IS THE CENTER OF FINANCE, ART, PUBLISHING, AND FASHION.

NOW, OVER TWO BILLION RIDERS USE IT YEARLY.

HUDSON RIVER

NEW YORK CITY WAS CONSIDERED THE CAPITAL OF THE U.S. FROM 1785 TO 1790.

IN 1789, GEORGE WASHINGTON TOOK HIS OATH OF OFFICE IN FEDERAL HALL AND BECAME OUR COUNTRY'S FIRST PRESIDENT.

THE STATUE OF LIBERTY WAS A GIFT TO THE U.S. FROM THE PEOPLE OF FRANCE.

WALL STREET IS THE NATION'S FINANCIAL CENTER.

RUNNING UNDER THE CITY ARE 60,000 MILES OF ELECTRICAL WIRING.

...AND 20 MILLION MILES OF TELEPHONE CABLE!

ITS FORMAL NAME IS "LIBERTY ENLIGHTENING THE WORLD."

MANHATTAN WAS BOUGHT FROM THE ALGONQUIN INDIANS FOR ABOUT $24 WORTH OF TRINKETS BY PETER MINUIT, A DUTCH GOVERNOR.

WELCOME, IMMIGRANTS TO THE U.S.

IT WAS CREATED BY AUGUSTE BARTHOLDI, A FRENCH SCULPTOR.

ABOUT HALF THE PEOPLE IN THE U.S. TODAY EITHER ARRIVED IN AMERICA THROUGH ELLIS ISLAND OR ARE DESCENDANTS OF SOMEONE WHO DID.

IN 1921, IMMIGRANTS ON ELLIS ISLAND WERE GIVEN A SPECIAL TREAT—ICE CREAM.

MOST HAD NEVER SEEN IT BEFORE AND THOUGHT IT WAS "NEW BUTTER" WHICH THEY SPREAD ON THEIR BREAD.

ELLIS ISLAND

I'M ON GOVERNORS ISLAND.

WE JUST VISITED THE STATUE OF LIBERTY.

I LIVE HERE TOO!

THAT'S MY HOME BOROUGH!

STATEN ISLAND

JOHN'S FERRY

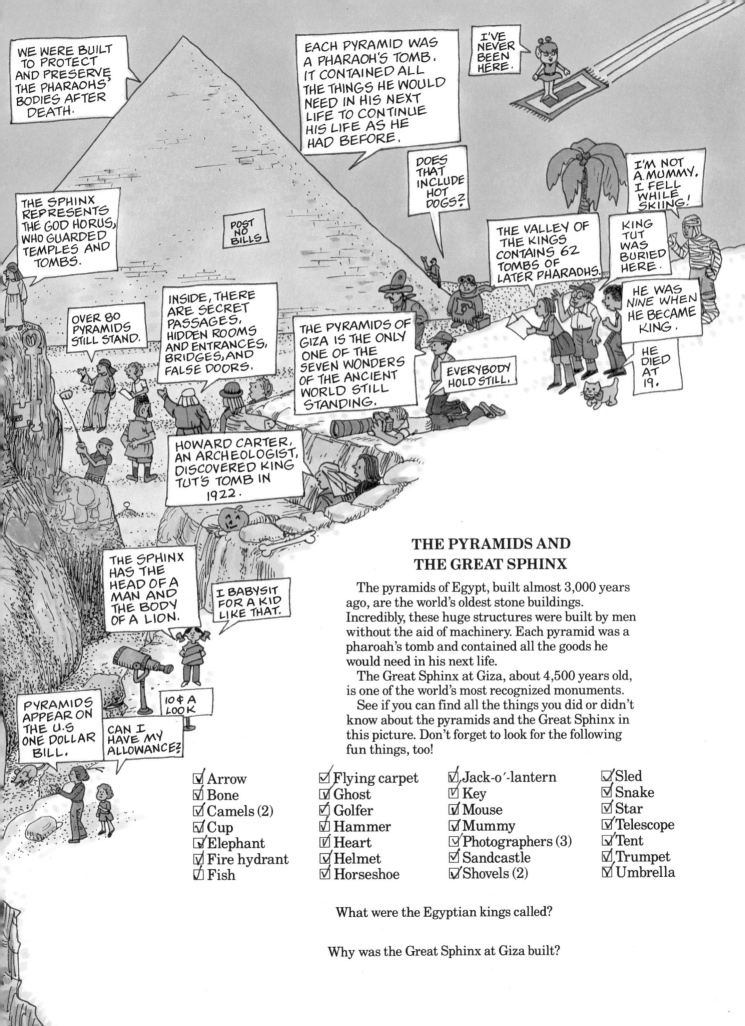

THE PYRAMIDS AND THE GREAT SPHINX

The pyramids of Egypt, built almost 3,000 years ago, are the world's oldest stone buildings. Incredibly, these huge structures were built by men without the aid of machinery. Each pyramid was a pharoah's tomb and contained all the goods he would need in his next life.

The Great Sphinx at Giza, about 4,500 years old, is one of the world's most recognized monuments.

See if you can find all the things you did or didn't know about the pyramids and the Great Sphinx in this picture. Don't forget to look for the following fun things, too!

☑ Arrow
☑ Bone
☑ Camels (2)
☑ Cup
☑ Elephant
☑ Fire hydrant
☑ Fish

☑ Flying carpet
☑ Ghost
☑ Golfer
☑ Hammer
☑ Heart
☑ Helmet
☑ Horseshoe

☑ Jack-o'-lantern
☑ Key
☑ Mouse
☑ Mummy
☑ Photographers (3)
☑ Sandcastle
☑ Shovels (2)

☑ Sled
☑ Snake
☑ Star
☑ Telescope
☑ Tent
☑ Trumpet
☑ Umbrella

What were the Egyptian kings called?

Why was the Great Sphinx at Giza built?

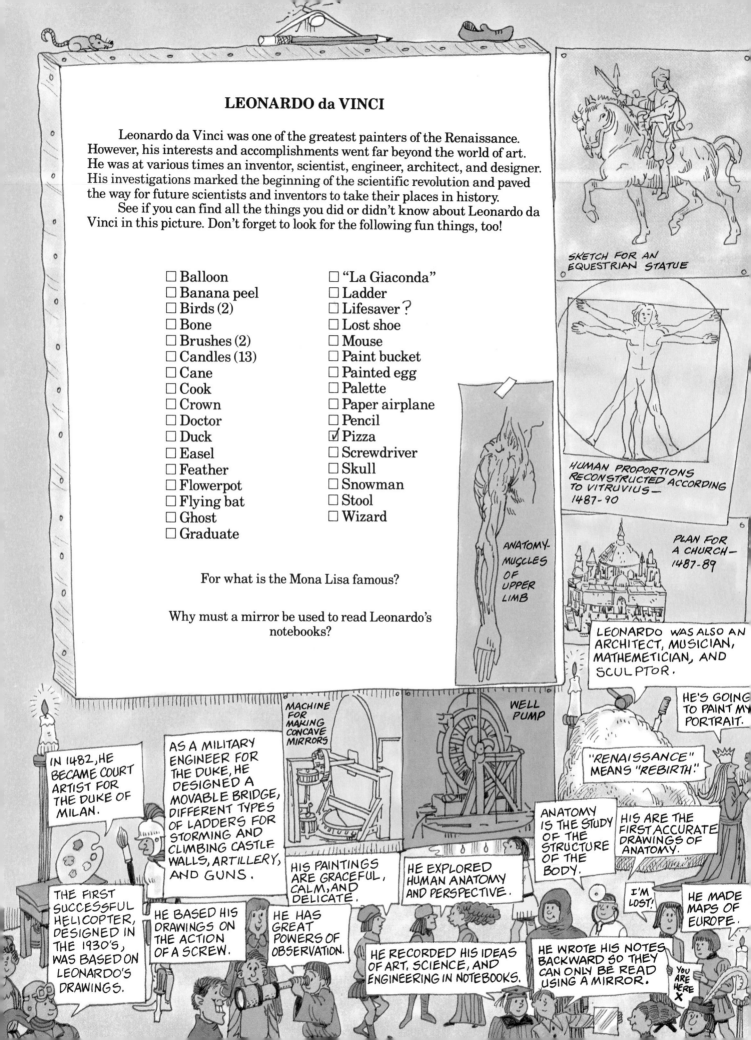

LEONARDO da VINCI

Leonardo da Vinci was one of the greatest painters of the Renaissance. However, his interests and accomplishments went far beyond the world of art. He was at various times an inventor, scientist, engineer, architect, and designer. His investigations marked the beginning of the scientific revolution and paved the way for future scientists and inventors to take their places in history.

See if you can find all the things you did or didn't know about Leonardo da Vinci in this picture. Don't forget to look for the following fun things, too!

- ☐ Balloon
- ☐ Banana peel
- ☐ Birds (2)
- ☐ Bone
- ☐ Brushes (2)
- ☐ Candles (13)
- ☐ Cane
- ☐ Cook
- ☐ Crown
- ☐ Doctor
- ☐ Duck
- ☐ Easel
- ☐ Feather
- ☐ Flowerpot
- ☐ Flying bat
- ☐ Ghost
- ☐ Graduate
- ☐ "La Giaconda"
- ☐ Ladder
- ☐ Lifesaver ?
- ☐ Lost shoe
- ☐ Mouse
- ☐ Paint bucket
- ☐ Painted egg
- ☐ Palette
- ☐ Paper airplane
- ☐ Pencil
- ☑ Pizza
- ☐ Screwdriver
- ☐ Skull
- ☐ Snowman
- ☐ Stool
- ☐ Wizard

For what is the Mona Lisa famous?

Why must a mirror be used to read Leonardo's notebooks?

SKETCH FOR AN EQUESTRIAN STATUE

HUMAN PROPORTIONS RECONSTRUCTED ACCORDING TO VITRUVIUS— 1487-90

ANATOMY- MUSCLES OF UPPER LIMB

PLAN FOR A CHURCH— 1487-89

LEONARDO WAS ALSO AN ARCHITECT, MUSICIAN, MATHEMETICIAN, AND SCULPTOR.

HE'S GOING TO PAINT MY PORTRAIT.

"RENAISSANCE" MEANS "REBIRTH."

MACHINE FOR MAKING CONCAVE MIRRORS

WELL PUMP

IN 1482, HE BECAME COURT ARTIST FOR THE DUKE OF MILAN.

AS A MILITARY ENGINEER FOR THE DUKE, HE DESIGNED A MOVABLE BRIDGE, DIFFERENT TYPES OF LADDERS FOR STORMING AND CLIMBING CASTLE WALLS, ARTILLERY, AND GUNS.

HIS PAINTINGS ARE GRACEFUL, CALM, AND DELICATE.

HE EXPLORED HUMAN ANATOMY AND PERSPECTIVE.

ANATOMY IS THE STUDY OF THE STRUCTURE OF THE BODY.

HIS ARE THE FIRST ACCURATE DRAWINGS OF ANATOMY.

THE FIRST SUCCESSFUL HELICOPTER, DESIGNED IN THE 1930'S, WAS BASED ON LEONARDO'S DRAWINGS.

HE BASED HIS DRAWINGS ON THE ACTION OF A SCREW.

HE HAS GREAT POWERS OF OBSERVATION.

HE RECORDED HIS IDEAS OF ART, SCIENCE, AND ENGINEERING IN NOTEBOOKS.

HE WROTE HIS NOTES BACKWARD SO THEY CAN ONLY BE READ USING A MIRROR.

I'M LOST!

HE MADE MAPS OF EUROPE.

YOU ARE HERE X

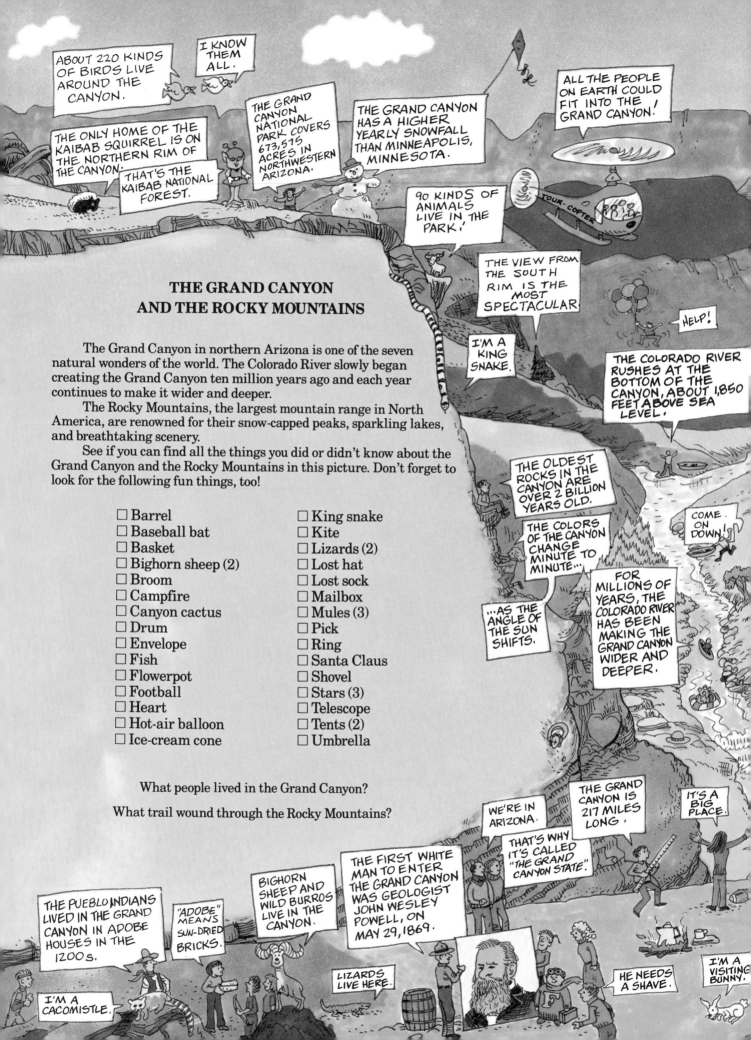

THE GRAND CANYON AND THE ROCKY MOUNTAINS

The Grand Canyon in northern Arizona is one of the seven natural wonders of the world. The Colorado River slowly began creating the Grand Canyon ten million years ago and each year continues to make it wider and deeper.

The Rocky Mountains, the largest mountain range in North America, are renowned for their snow-capped peaks, sparkling lakes, and breathtaking scenery.

See if you can find all the things you did or didn't know about the Grand Canyon and the Rocky Mountains in this picture. Don't forget to look for the following fun things, too!

☐ Barrel
☐ Baseball bat
☐ Basket
☐ Bighorn sheep (2)
☐ Broom
☐ Campfire
☐ Canyon cactus
☐ Drum
☐ Envelope
☐ Fish
☐ Flowerpot
☐ Football
☐ Heart
☐ Hot-air balloon
☐ Ice-cream cone
☐ King snake
☐ Kite
☐ Lizards (2)
☐ Lost hat
☐ Lost sock
☐ Mailbox
☐ Mules (3)
☐ Pick
☐ Ring
☐ Santa Claus
☐ Shovel
☐ Stars (3)
☐ Telescope
☐ Tents (2)
☐ Umbrella

What people lived in the Grand Canyon?

What trail wound through the Rocky Mountains?

CHRISTOPHER COLUMBUS

Christopher Columbus was one of the greatest explorers of all time. In 1492, he left Spain and set sail for Asia with his three ships, the Nina, the Pinta, and the Santa Maria. Columbus never made it to the East Indies. Instead, he discovered the New World which is known today as the Americas.

See if you can find all the things you did or didn't know about Christopher Columbus. Don't forget to look for the following fun things, too!

- ☐ Arrows (2)
- ☐ Barrel
- ☐ Basket
- ☐ Bone
- ☐ Duck
- ☐ Egg
- ☑ Fish (4)
- ☐ Flower
- ☐ Hummingbird
- ☐ Jack-o'-lantern
- ☐ Key
- ☐ Laundry
- ☐ Moustache
- ☐ Octopus
- ☐ Parrot
- ☐ Periscope
- ☐ Pig
- ☐ Sea serpent
- ☐ Sick sailor
- ☐ Snake
- ☐ Spaceship
- ☐ Spears
- ☐ Sword
- ☐ T-shirt
- ☐ Telescope
- ☐ Tire
- ☐ Turtle
- ☐ Wooden leg

Who helped finance the trip?

How many voyages did Columbus make?

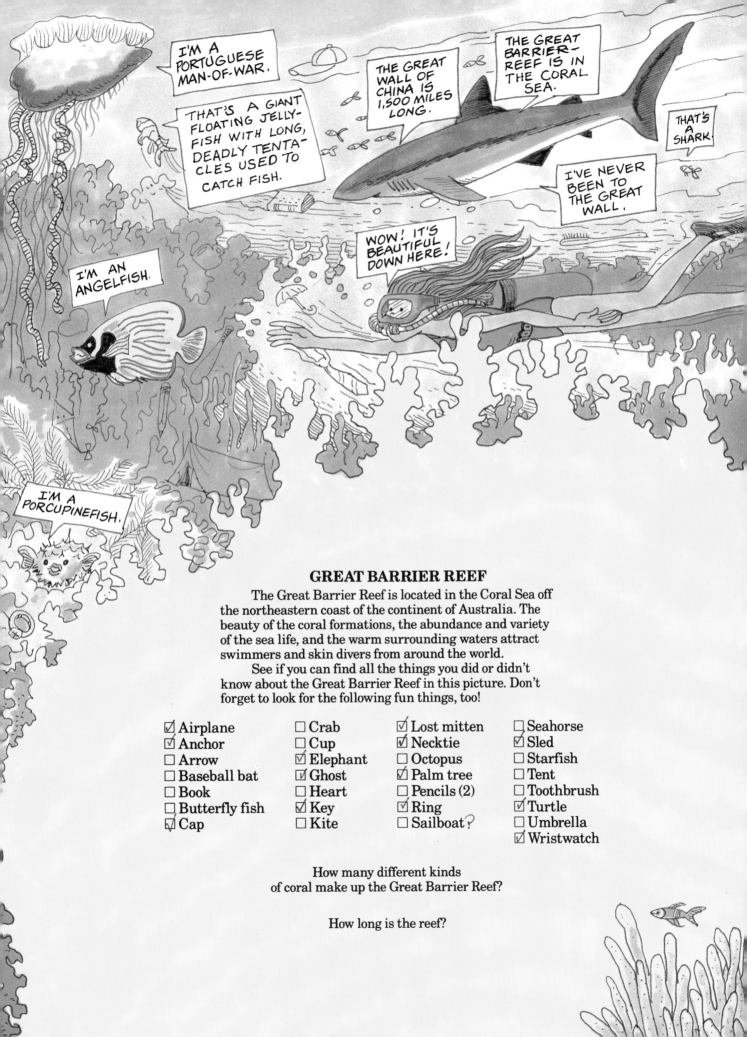

GREAT BARRIER REEF

The Great Barrier Reef is located in the Coral Sea off the northeastern coast of the continent of Australia. The beauty of the coral formations, the abundance and variety of the sea life, and the warm surrounding waters attract swimmers and skin divers from around the world.

See if you can find all the things you did or didn't know about the Great Barrier Reef in this picture. Don't forget to look for the following fun things, too!

☑ Airplane
☑ Anchor
☐ Arrow
☐ Baseball bat
☐ Book
☐ Butterfly fish
☑ Cap
☐ Crab
☐ Cup
☑ Elephant
☑ Ghost
☐ Heart
☑ Key
☐ Kite
☑ Lost mitten
☑ Necktie
☐ Octopus
☑ Palm tree
☐ Pencils (2)
☑ Ring
☐ Sailboat
☐ Seahorse
☑ Sled
☐ Starfish
☐ Tent
☐ Toothbrush
☑ Turtle
☐ Umbrella
☑ Wristwatch

How many different kinds
of coral make up the Great Barrier Reef?

How long is the reef?